Foxes, weasels and badgers

DeAGOSTINI

Who am I?

MY EARS
They are flat and rounded.
I have very good hearing.

MY EYES
My eyes are large
and black, and I have
fantastic eyesight.

MY NOSE
I have a great
sense of smell.

MY BELLY
I have white fur that
runs all the way down my
neck and onto my body.

Hello, everyone! My name is Harry and I'm a weasel.
I'm a wild animal and usually live in the woods.

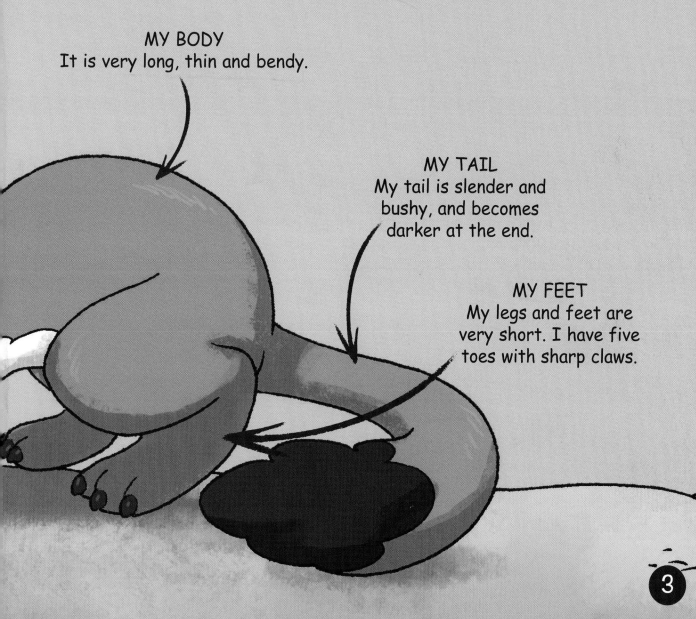

MY BODY
It is very long, thin and bendy.

MY TAIL
My tail is slender and
bushy, and becomes
darker at the end.

MY FEET
My legs and feet are
very short. I have five
toes with sharp claws.

Where do I live?

I am found in forests and woodland, where there is plenty of undergrowth. I live in burrows and nests, but I do not create my own. I usually move into homes that have been abandoned by my prey. It is here that I have my babies, and I bring them food that I have hunted in the field.

What do I eat?

I like to eat mice, hares, birds and even eggs. My slim and agile body makes me an excellent hunter, as I can move very quickly. I can jump, run fast and climb trees easily. When I sense that food is nearby, I sometimes stand on my back legs to see my prey. Then, I dart after it!

Who am I?

MY EARS
They are small, but
I have good hearing.

MY HEAD
It is long and white,
with a broad black
stripe on either side.

MY NOSE
I have a long snout and
brilliant sense of smell.

MY CHEST
My neck, chest and stomach
area are completely black.

Hello, everyone! My name is Boris and I'm a boar - that is the name given to a male badger. Let me tell you about my family.

MY FUR
It is long with a mixture of grey tones.

MY TAIL
I have a short, flat tail.

MY FEET
They are very strong. I have sharp claws to help me dig my home underground.

THE SOW
I'm a lot like the male. I have lots of little cubs.

THE CUB
I am the baby of the boar and the sow. I can have around two to five brothers and sisters each year.

Where do I live?

I mainly like to live in sheltered areas, such as forests and on the edge of fields. I dig my burrow underground to keep me safe. This is my home – it's called a sett. I sleep during the day and go out at night to look for food.

What do I eat?

I eat worms, mice, birds, eggs and insects. I also love fruit and vegetables. The best way to get these is to sneak into vegetable plots and fruit gardens late at night. I look for holes in the fence or areas where I can burrow underneath. I'm not a picky eater and consume almost anything I find!

Who am I?

MY EARS
My hearing is really good. It's about twelve times better than yours!

MY EYES
I have very good eyesight.

MY NOSE
I have a long pointed snout and a great sense of smell.

MY LEGS AND FEET
I have long thin legs, with small feet and claws. The fur on my legs gets darker as it nears my feet.

Hello! My name is Fenton and I'm a male fox. A male fox is called a dog and I'm a very clever wild animal.

MY HAIR
My hair is very thick and reddish-brown in colour.

THE VIXEN
I am a female fox. I look similar to the male and it is hard to tell us apart.

MY TAIL
I am famous for having a big bushy tail.

THE KIT
I am the baby of the dog and the vixen. I love to play and usually have two or three brothers and sisters.

Where do I live?

I mainly live in forests and wooded areas, but I like to wander across the countryside. I also like anywhere I can get food, including parks and gardens. I live in a burrow – foxes' burrows are called dens. I can dig my own den or use one that has been abandoned by another animal. I normally come out at night and sneak around in the dark.

What do I eat?

I am very fast and cunning. I'm good at catching other animals and especially like to eat mice and rabbits when I'm hunting in the wild. I can dig my way under the farmer's fence and catch chickens, too. I can climb trees and I'm also a really terrific swimmer.

The dangerous fox

When foxes live near farms, we can be very dangerous. When we can't find food in the forest or fields, we creep into the farm and eat anything we can find, including chickens, eggs and rabbits.

PEOPLE AND FOXES

In some places, like the USA and southern Europe, foxes can carry a dangerous disease called rabies. But if you live in the UK, Ireland, Australia or New Zealand, don't worry - there are no rabid foxes in your country. Even so, it's a good idea to keep young babies away from foxes.

The hunt

When badgers, weasels and foxes get together, we can cause a lot of trouble for the farmer. When this happens he heads into the field to try and track us down.

NICE AND SAFE!

The farmer has to protect his animals. At night, he shuts all of them safely in their cages to stop any badgers, weasels or foxes from catching them.

Bump in the night

Everyone was asleep on Happy Acre Farm. All except two very crafty and hungry creatures.

"Poor me!" shouted Harry, the weasel. "It's been three days since I last had a meal. I'm so hungry."

"Shh!" whispered Fenton, the fox. "You don't want to wake up the whole farm do you?"

Harry and Fenton were good friends. After all, they often prowled around the farm when it was dark, searching for a midnight snack.

"I'm here to try and catch some chickens," said Fenton. "What have you come for?"

"I'm just glad I made it here," whimpered Harry. "My poor, poor tummy! It hurts."

"Will you stop feeling sorry for yourself!" said Fenton. "Maybe if we put our heads together we could catch something tasty. How about these two mice?" Fenton continued, whilst pointing at the little creatures scurrying around in the hay.

"I have an even better plan!" whispered Harry, as an idea suddenly hit him. "We could catch some chickens together."

"Those chickens were all going to be for me!" replied Fenton, the fox.

"If we work together we could catch them quicker," said Harry.

Fenton needed time to think. He wasn't used about working as a team. But then, the idea excited him.

The fox and the weasel both thought about all the chickens they could catch togther. It would be so much easier!

"Okay!" Fenton finally announced. "Let's do it."

"We'll need a big run up if we're going to get enough speed to outwit those chickens," said Harry.

So, Fenton and Harry both crept to either end of the farm.

"Ready?" cried Fenton.

"Steady?" shouted Harry.

"GO!" they bellowed together.

They both put their heads down and ran towards the chicken coop as fast as they could. The chickens woke up just in time to see Fenton and Harry go charging into each other with an

almighty BANG!

"Ouch!" cried Harry.

"You silly fool!" shouted Fenton. "That wasn't quite what I meant by putting our heads together!"

All the noise awoke George, the farmer, who was sleeping in his bed. He dashed into the farmyard and Fenton and Harry ran off into the night... still hungry!

The end

The little lamb

It was a wonderful day for taking the sheep into the mountains. The field they had been grazing in was becoming low on grass, so it was time to move the herd for the summer.

The shepherd rounded up the sheep and decided to have a good talk to them before they headed off.

"The mountains are a fantastic place," he said. "But they can be dangerous too, especially after dark. Sometimes, there are wolves lurking in the forest, so you must all stick together as a herd wherever we go."

The sheep all nodded, except one.

Amongst the sheep was a little lamb. He had never been to the mountains before, and the entire journey was a big adventure. "I don't want to stick with the herd," he said. "There's more fun to be had on my own."

So, as the sheep headed up the mountainside, the little lamb began to stray. He discovered thistles, a groundhog and saw some unusual shaped rocks that he had never seen before.

Then he saw a beautiful butterfly and chased it for most of the afternoon until he was a long way from the other sheep. By the end of the day, the lamb was so tired he found a nice shaded spot underneath a tree and fell asleep.

Time passed by - more time than the lamb had realised. Suddenly, he

felt something hit his nose. It was a drop of rain. He opened his eyes to discover that all the sheep had gone. Not only that, it was dark and raining.

The poor little lamb was cold, wet and all alone in the night... well, almost all alone!

In the darkness a creature lurked. It prowled around the trees, sniffing out the little lamb.

"Oh, no!" bleated the lamb. "It's the wolf. It's come to gobble me up!"

"Not quite," replied the voice. "I've been looking for you everywhere."

It was the sheepdog. He knew the lamb had been left behind and had been searching for him.

"Come on!" barked the sheepdog. "Let's get back to the herd."

So, the lamb ran beside the sheepdog up the mountain and snuggled as close as he could to the other sheep.

"It's great exploring," said the lamb. "But it's even better being part of the herd."

That night, the lamb slept better than he ever had before.

The end

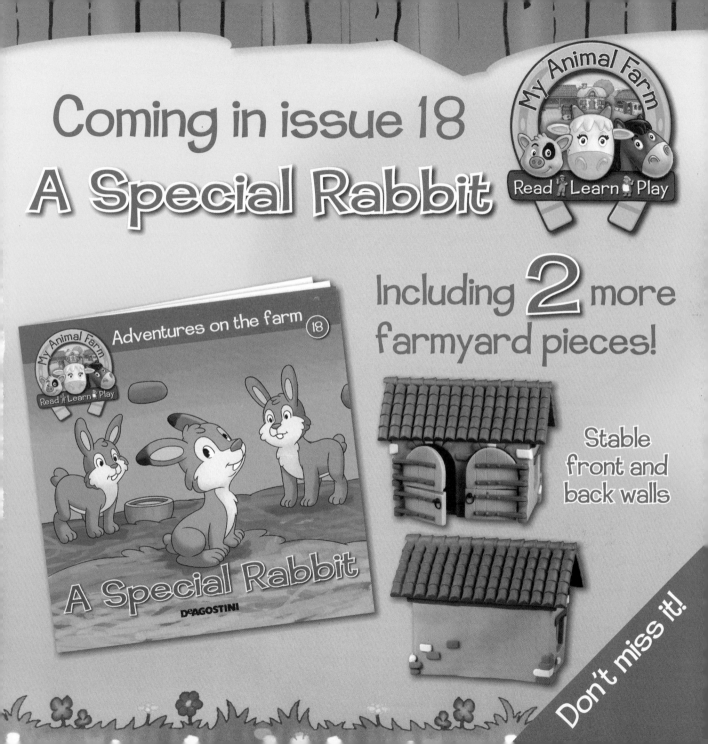